A boy called Marshall

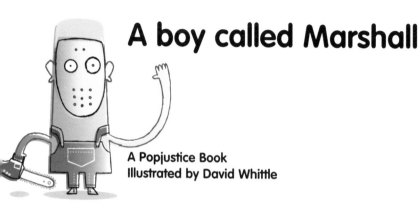

A boy called Marshall

A Popjustice Book
Illustrated by David Whittle

First published in Great Britain in 2006 by Friday Books
An imprint of The Friday Project Limited
83 Victoria Street, London SW1H 0HW

www.thefridayproject.co.uk
www.fridaybooks.co.uk

Text © Peter Robinson 2006
Illustrations © David Whittle 2006

ISBN – 10   0 9548318 6 1
ISBN – 13   978 0 9548318 6 8

British Library Cataloguing in Publication Data

A catalogue record for this book is available
from the British Library

Designed and produced by Staziker Jones
www.stazikerjones.co.uk

The Publisher's policy is to use paper
manufactured from sustainable sources

This book belongs to

_____

I am ____ years old

My favourite Eminem song is _____

When I grow up, I want to be _____

Here is my autograph

_____

This is Marshall.

Marshall is what he says he is.

If he wasn't, then why would he say he was?

When Marshall was a small boy, he lived in a very special house.

The house was on wheels!

Marshall liked to rap.

One day he entered a competition called the Rap Olympics.

He got the silver medal for a song he made up on the spot.

If he had practised beforehand maybe he would have got gold!

HaMMeRtiMe

When he was a grown-up, Marshall went to the doctor. But this was a very special doctor, with magic powers.

The doctor said to Marshall: 'I will make you the most famous little boy in the world'.

Marshall liked this idea. 'It's a deal!' he said.

To become famous, Marshall only had to sing some songs.

In one song, he put a car into the sea.

But there was somebody still inside the car!

Some people said that it was a dangerous thing to do, but Marshall did not say sorry.

Marshall did not like saying sorry. And he always had to tell the truth.

As you can imagine, sometimes this got him into trouble.

Some people protested and demonstrated against Marshall.

But other people liked him.

Marshall liked to dress up.

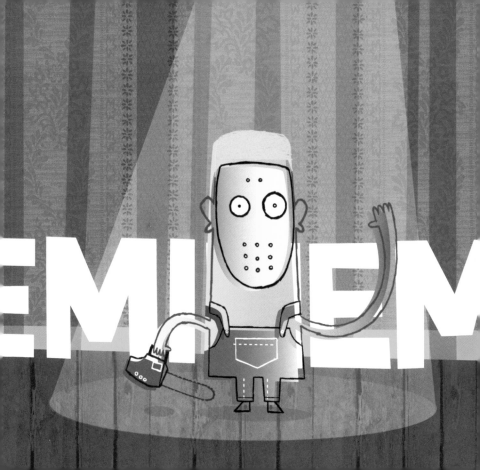

On his travels, Marshall met a man named Elton.

Elton was a very famous singer from a place very very far away.

Elton liked to wear pink clothes and Marshall did not, but they still made friends!

Another time, Marshall became pen pals with a boy!

The boy's name was Stan.

Stan wrote Marshall lots and lots of letters, but Marshall did not get them.

There must have been a problem at the post office or something!

Stan fell off a bridge.

This made Marshall sad, because he had just started writing a letter to Stan!

Marshall became very serious.

Everyone knew Marshall was serious – because he wore his spectacles in a pop video!

One day Marshall heard a lady singing.

She called herself Dido, but her real name was Florian Cloud de Bounevialle Armstrong.

It was an interesting name for a very interesting lady!

Marshall turned Florian Cloud de Bounevialle Armstrong into a famous singer.

Marshall liked to make lots of his friends famous, just as the magic doctor had made him famous.

One time, he invited some of them to sing some songs with him – and he did not even mind that they could not sing very well!

That just goes to show you what a nice person Marshall was.

Another of Marshall's friends was very special indeed. He called himself 50 Cent, but his real name was Curtis.

No matter how much people tried to hurt Curtis, he did not get poorly!

Curtis did not like to talk about it, but he had nine holes in his body!

Or ten, if you include his bottom.

When he was 31 years old, Marshall decided he did not like the person in charge of America.

He sang a very angry song about just that.

He wanted people to hear it and ask for a new person to be in charge!

Nothing changed.

As he got older, Marshall carried on working very hard.

He always had so many exciting thoughts in his head that sometimes he needed some special sweets to help him sleep.

Unfortunately Marshall ate too many magic sweets!

He went to see a different doctor.

The doctor said that as a punishment he could not go on holiday to England.

This second doctor was not as much fun as Marshall's first doctor, but he made Marshall better again.

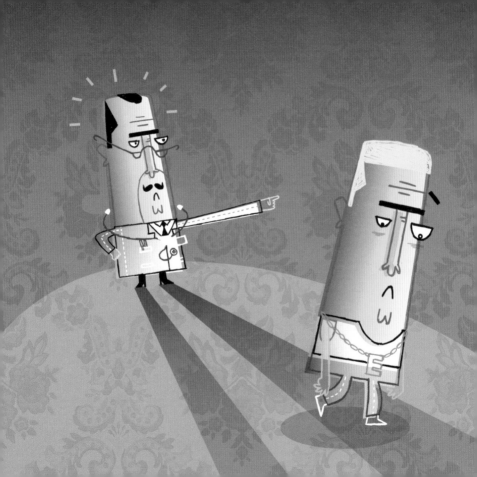

Marshall was as famous as famous could be. Because of this, Marshall was a happy man.

These days, Marshall lives in a very big house – it is not on wheels, but he likes it a lot!

Marshall and Dre like to play doctors together!

Cut around the edges (be careful with the scissors!), stick Marshall and Dre to your fingers and act out scenes.

Marshall: What are you wearing underneath your trousers?
Dre: Knickers with attitude.

Have fun!

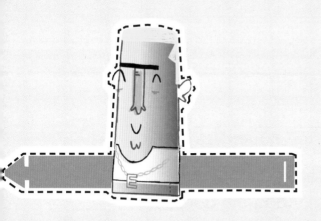

Popjustice.com is the greatest pop website on the face of Planet Earth. We update every day with the best pop stuff.

Drop in at **www.popjustice.com/idols** for downloadable wallpapers, screensavers and other random nonsense.

Why not send us an email? idols@popjustice.com